Two Mums and a Menagerie

Written by Carolyn Robertson

Illustrated by Patricia de Villiers

Published 2015 by Sparklypoo Publications London UK

www.sparklypoo.com

For Bobby and Jacob

with much love

On the edge of a city lived two mums and their son.

The son they'd adopted was Son Number One.

Son Number One was their

first special boy.

He giggled and gurgled

and filled them with joy.

The three lived happily with fun days galore.

Until they all said

"Let's make room for one more!

We've got plenty of space and plenty of love."

And Son Number One said

"I'd quite like a bruv."

So very soon the three became four,

When Son Number Two arrived through the door.

Son Number Two made their family complete.

He was smiley and cute

and quick on his feet.

They played and they worked, they sang and they danced.

They loved and they laughed and giggled and pranked.

Their home was a jumble of toys, books and games.

They loved baking and making, or dens when it rained.

Then a neighbour popped round with a fluffy black bundle,

Saying "She needs someone to love her and stop her tum rumble.

I found her outside, so frightened and small,

She was sitting on top of my front garden wall."

The four scratched their chins and the mums were divided.

But the boys, they were sure,

so it was decided,

To adopt the poor cat and give her a home.

They just couldn't leave her, so small and alone.

Cats, boys and mummies lived together in peace,

'Til an uncle came round with a dog on a leash.

"My flat is too small for this doggie I found.

I thought you might like him, he's such a cute hound."

The mummies said "No! We haven't the space."

(But both boys had mastered their puppy dog face)

"We'll stroke him and feed him and take him for walks."

"And picking up poos?" said Mummies.

"Of course!"

One bright Sunday morning on a walk in the park,

They heard a strange noise... a squeak or a squawk?

It came from the bush by the side of the lake.

A mouse or a duck? A goose or a drake?

Son Number One was an animal whizz.

He said "I'll explore and find out what it is."

He emerged from the shrubs with a spiky, tight ball.

A tiny brown hedgehog
who'd taken a fall.

The hedgehog moved in and over the weeks,

He was joined by two field mice, a hen and three geese.

The house was beginning to look like a zoo,

With fur balls and feathers and sacks full of poo.

Hamsters and guinea pigs roamed in their cages.

Spiders and snakes hung about
in weird places.

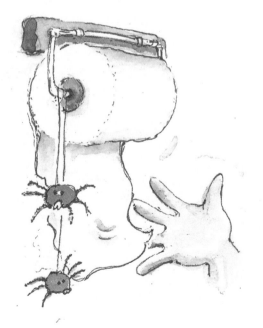

A lizard, called Lispy, lived under the stairs.

He frightened their grandma who jumped onto chairs.

Over the months as the family expanded,

It all got too much and one mummy demanded

"That's it. I simply can't take anymore.

We've not enough room to open the door!

Let's move to the country, with a barn and a field."

The boys ears pricked up, this prospect appealed.

The dens they could build! The animals they'd keep!

There'd be horses and cows, chickens and sheep.

The mummies agreed, city life had them beat.

The rushing around the cars and the heat.

So they packed up their things,

said goodbye to their neighbours.

And swapped city life for two sunny acres.

They had space to run and space to roam.

The animals were delighted with their new home.

They all lived together, this special family.

Two boys, their mums...

and a menagerie.

About The Author

Carolyn and her partner are adoptive mums to two fabulous boys. Carolyn is a school teacher and author. She lives and works in South London, UK.

@carolynadopt

Printed in Great Britain
by Amazon